PERSEUS

THE HUNT FOR MEDUSA'S HEAD

A GREEK MYTH

STORY BY
PAUL D STORRIE

PENCILS AND INKS BY
THOMAS YEATES

EUROPE

AFRICA

PERSEUS

THE HUNT FOR MEDUSA'S HEAD

A
GREEK
MYTH

GREECE

TURKEY

ARGOS

SERIPHUS

MEDITERRANEAN SEA

LERNER BOOKS · LONDON · NEW YORK · MINNEAPOLIS

Perseus is one of the greatest heroes of Greek literature. The legendary feats of Zeus' son have been passed down from generation to generation for more than two thousand years. To create the Graphic Myths and Legends version of Perseus' story, author Paul Storrie relied heavily on both Thomas Bulfinch's The Age of Fable, first published in 1859, and Edith Hamilton's Mythology, first published in 1942. Both of these well-known works drew their material from the writings of the ancient poets such as Ovid and Virgil. Artist Thomas Yeates consulted numerous historical and traditional sources to give the art an authentic feel, from classical Greek architecture to the clothing, weapons and armour worn by the characters. Professor David Mulroy of the University of Wisconsin-Milwaukee, USA, ensured historical and visual accuracy.

STORY BY PAUL D STORRIE

PENCILS AND INKS BY THOMAS YEATES
WITH TOD SMITH AND KEN HOOPER

COLOURING BY HI-FI COLOUR DESIGN

LETTERING BY INTERFACE GRAPHICS, INC.

CONSULTANT: DAVID MULROY, PhD
UNIVERSITY OF WISCONSIN-MILWAUKEE

Graphic Universe™ is a trademark of Lerner Publishing Group, Inc.

First published in the United Kingdom in 2009 by
Lerner Books,
Dalton House,
60 Windsor Avenue,
London SW19 2RR

Website: www.lernerbooks.co.uk

This edition was updated and edited for UK publication by Discovery Books Ltd., First Floor, 2 College Street, Ludlow, Shropshire SY8 1AN

British Library Cataloguing in Publication Data

Storrie, Paul D.
    Perseus : the hunt for the Medusa's head. - 2nd ed. - (Graphic universe)
    1. Perseus (Greek mythology) - Comic books, strips, etc. - Juvenile fiction
    2. Children's stories - Comic books, strips, etc.
    I. Title II. Yeates, Thomas
    741.5

ISBN-13: 978 0 7613 4349 3

Printed in Singapore

TABLE OF CONTENTS

AN UNEXPECTED VISIT

LONG YEARS AGO, IN THE LAND OF GREECE, A YOUNG HERO NAMED PERSEUS FOUND HIMSELF FACED WITH A TERRIBLE TASK. HE KNEW THAT IF HE ACCOMPLISHED WHAT HE WAS SETTING OUT TO DO, HIS FAME WOULD LAST FOREVER.

THAT IS, IF HE SURVIVED ...

7

MEDUSA IS A HIDEOUS CREATURE, AND HER VERY GAZE CAN TURN YOU TO STONE. LOOK ONLY AT HER REFLECTION IN THIS SHIELD, AND YOU WILL BE SAFE.

THE SICKLE IS FORMED OF ADAMANTINE, STRONGEST OF SUBSTANCES. WITH IT YOU CAN STRIKE OFF HER HEAD WITH ONE STROKE! IT IS A GIFT FROM HERMES, MESSENGER OF THE GODS, AS ARE THE WINGED SANDALS THAT WILL LET YOU FLY SWIFTLY OVER THE LONG DISTANCES OF YOUR JOURNEY.

THE HELMET BELONGS TO HADES, LORD OF THE UNDER-WORLD. WHEN YOU LOWER IT OVER YOUR FACE, YOU WILL BE INVISIBLE!

AND LAST, A MAGIC SATCHEL IN WHICH YOU CAN SAFELY CARRY THE HEAD.

WITH THESE GIFTS, I CANNOT FAIL!

THAT IS, IF I KNEW WHERE TO FIND MEDUSA.

EVEN I CANNOT TELL YOU THAT. BUT I KNOW WHO CAN.

GRATEFUL FOR HER HELP, PERSEUS LISTENED CLOSELY TO ALL ATHENA HAD TO TELL HIM.

BUT TO UNDERSTAND WHY THE GODS TOOK AN INTEREST IN PERSEUS, IT IS IMPORTANT TO KNOW THE STORY OF HIS BIRTH.

THE CRUELTY
OF TWO KINGS

YEARS BEFORE, AN ORACLE HAD TOLD KING ACRISIUS OF ARGOS THAT HE WOULD DIE AT THE HANDS OF HIS GRANDSON.

TO KEEP THAT FROM HAPPENING, HE HAD A TALL TOWER BUILT TO LOCK AWAY HIS BEAUTIFUL DAUGHTER, DANAË.

THOUGH DANAË PLEADED WITH HER FATHER NOT TO SHUT HER IN THE TOWER, HE WAS CONVINCED IT WAS THE ONLY WAY TO STOP THE PROPHECY FROM COMING TRUE.

EXCEPT FOR THE KING, ONLY WOMEN WERE ALLOWED IN THE TOWER TO BRING THE PRINCESS WHAT SHE NEEDED. THE KING'S PLAN SEEMED FOOLPROOF. WITH NO MEN COMING NEAR HER, SHE WOULD NEVER BE ABLE TO BEAR A CHILD.

BUT SHE COULD NOT KEEP THE SECRET FOREVER. ACRISIUS WAS TERRIFIED WHEN HE LEARNED THAT HER BABY WAS THE SON OF ZEUS.

CAUGHT BETWEEN THE PROPHECY AND THE WRATH OF ZEUS, ACRISIUS DECIDED TO PUT THE LIVES OF DANAË AND HER BABY, PERSEUS, IN THE HANDS OF FATE.

HE HOPED THAT IF THEY WERE TAKEN BY THE SEA, THE GODS WOULD NOT HOLD HIM ACCOUNTABLE.

BUT ZEUS KNEW WHAT HAD HAPPENED. HE ASKED HIS BROTHER POSEIDON, GOD OF THE SEA, TO SEND A STORM TO GUIDE HIS SON TO SAFETY.

NEAR THE ISLAND KINGDOM OF SERIPHUS, A FISHERMAN NAMED DICTYS WAS CAUGHT OUT IN THE STORM.

SNAGGING THE CHEST WITH ONE OF HIS NETS, HE DRAGGED IT TO SHORE. HE WAS ASTOUNDED TO FIND OUT WHAT IT CONTAINED!

WHEN HE HEARD DANAË'S STORY, DICTYS IMMEDIATELY TOOK HER TO SEE HIS BROTHER, KING POLYDECTES.

EVEN THOUGH SERIPHUS WAS SUCH A SMALL KINGDOM THAT THE KING'S BROTHER HAD TO WORK AS A FISHERMAN, POLYDECTES THOUGHT OF HIMSELF AS A GREAT RULER.

HE IMMEDIATELY SAW THAT HAVING THE BEAUTIFUL DANAË AS HIS QUEEN WOULD MAKE HIM THE ENVY OF ANY KING.

POLYDECTES TOOK DANAË AND HER SON INTO HIS HOME.

HE DID EVERYTHING HE COULD TO TRY TO MAKE HER LOVE HIM.

NOTHING HE DID WORKED. ALTHOUGH DANAË WAS THANKFUL FOR HIS GENEROSITY, SHE REFUSED TO CONSIDER MARRYING HIM.

AS PERSEUS GREW OLDER, HE DID HIS BEST TO HELP HIS MOTHER KEEP THE KING AT A DISTANCE.

AS ONE WOULD EXPECT OF ZEUS' SON, PERSEUS BECAME A GREAT ATHLETE AND WARRIOR.

BECAUSE OF THAT, POLYDECTES BEGAN TO FEAR HIM.

13

BUT POLYDECTES WAS CUNNING. HE CAME UP WITH A PLAN TO GET RID OF PERSEUS. THAT WAY DANAË WOULD HAVE TO RELY UPON THE KING FOR STRENGTH AND PROTECTION.

SINCE YOUR MOTHER STILL DOES NOT WISH TO MARRY ME, I HAVE DECIDED TO PROPOSE TO HIPPODAMIA, THE DAUGHTER OF KING PELOPS.

THAT'S WONDERFUL! I HOPE THE TWO OF YOU WILL BE HAPPY TOGETHER.

IT'S NOT SO SIMPLE, PERSEUS. PELOPS RULES A GREAT LAND. MANY KINGS WISH TO MARRY HIS DAUGHTER.

ALL THE MEN O SERIPHUS HAVE GIVEN ME FINE HORSES TO PRESE AS A GIFT TO PRO TO HIPPODAMIA AN HER FATHER THAT I AND MY KINGDOM ARE WORTHY.

I HAVE NO HORSES TO GIVE, BUT ASK ME FOR ANYTHING, AND I PROMISE THAT I WILL GET IT FOR YOU!

ANYTHING?

THE HUNT FOR MEDUSA'S HEAD

AND SO THE KING MADE PERSEUS PROMISE TO FETCH THE HEAD OF THE GORGON MEDUSA. POLYDECTES WAS CERTAIN THAT PERSEUS WOULD NEVER RETURN FROM HIS JOURNEY.

THE YOUNG HERO HOPED THAT THE WEAPONS PROVIDED BY THE GODS WOULD BE ENOUGH TO HELP HIM PROVE POLYDECTES WRONG.

ALTHOUGH SHE COULD NOT TELL PERSEUS WHERE TO FIND MEDUSA, ATHENA TOLD HIM WHO COULD.

THE THREE SISTERS, KNOWN AS THE GRAEAE, OR GREY-HAIRED ONES, WERE RELATED TO THE GORGONS. THE GRAEAE WERE SO OLD, THEY HAD ONLY ONE GOOD EYE AND ONE GOOD TOOTH BETWEEN THEM. BUT ATHENA WAS CERTAIN THAT THEY WOULD KNOW WHERE TO FIND MEDUSA AND HER SISTERS.

GIVE ME THE EYE!

IT'S MY TURN TO SEE!

I'M HUNGRY. I WANT THE TOOTH NOW!

16

PERSEUS WISHED HE COULD USE THE HELMET OF HADES TO APPROACH THE GORGONS.

UNFORTUNATELY, IT MADE EVERYTHING HE TOUCHED INVISIBLE TOO, INCLUDING HIS SHIELD. HE REMEMBERED ATHENA'S WARNING TO ONLY LOOK AT MEDUSA'S REFLECTION.

SINCE MEDUSA'S IMMORTAL SISTERS BOTH HAD HUGE, METALLIC WINGS, IT WASN'T HARD FOR PERSEUS TO CHOOSE THE RIGHT ONE.

VWHHHSSSSSSST!!

PERSEUS HAD TO STRIKE SWIFTLY, BEFORE MEDUSA COULD WAKE HER SISTERS!

ANDROMEDA AND THE KRAKEN

ON HIS WAY HOME, PERSEUS CAUGHT SIGHT OF SOMETHING THAT CONFUSED AND ALARMED HIM.

WHO ARE YOU, BEAUTIFUL LADY? WHO CHAINED YOU HERE AND WHY?

I AM THE PRINCESS ANDROMEDA, DAUGHTER OF KING CEPHEUS AND QUEEN CASSIOPEIA OF ETHIOPIA! THOUGH I DO NOT WISH TO DIE, I AM HERE FOR THE GOOD OF MY PEOPLE.

24

IF YOU DID KILL THE KRAKEN, THAT MIGHT ANGER POSEIDON EVEN MORE.

IF SO, HE WILL BE ANGRY WITH ME INSTEAD OF YOU! I AM ZEUS' SON AND HAVE THE FAVOUR OF ATHENA, HERMES AND EVEN HADES. I WILL TAKE THE RISK.

KING CEPHEUS, LOOK!

THE KRAKEN COMES!!!

THERE IS NO MORE TIME! SAVE ANDROMEDA! SAVE HER, AND SHE WILL BE YOUR WIFE!

DO YOU HEAR, ANDROMEDA? YOU WILL NOT DIE TODAY!

CHING!

BE CAREFUL, PERSEUS! DEFEAT THE KRAKEN, AND COME BACK TO ME!

THE WEDDING OF PERSEUS AND ANDROMEDA

ANDROMEDA INSISTED THAT SHE AND PERSEUS BE WED AT ONCE.

THE KING AND QUEEN WERE NOT AS JOYOUS AS THEIR SUBJECTS AND ANDROMEDA.

THOUGH THEY WERE PLEASED THAT THE HERO HAD SAVED THEIR DAUGHTER, THEY FOUND THEMSELVES MARRYING HER TO A TOTAL STRANGER.

AFTER THE BATTLE THE HAPPY COUPLE LIVED IN PEACE UNTIL...

DO YOU REALLY HAVE TO GO?

I PROMISED MEDUSA'S HEAD TO KING POLYDECTES.

THEN LET ME COME WITH YOU!

I CANNOT CARRY YOU WHILE I FLY.

BESIDES, I HAVE NO HOME OF MY OWN THERE. MY MOTHER AND I STAY IN THE PALACE, BUT ONLY AS GUESTS.

KING POLYDECTES HAS BEEN TRYING TO FORCE MY MOTHER TO MARRY HIM FOR YEARS. HE SAYS HE PLANS TO MARRY SOMEONE ELSE, BUT I DON'T TRUST HIM.

IT WILL BE BETTER IF I BRING MY MOTHER HERE, WHERE WE ARE ENTITLED TO LIVE IN THE PALACE AS FAMILY.

BE SAFE, PERSEUS! COME BACK TO ME SOON!

THE FATE OF FOUR KINGS

THE FIRST THING PERSEUS DID WHEN HE RETURNED TO SERIPHUS WAS VISIT THE TEMPLE TO GIVE THANKS TO THE GODS. HE KNEW THAT IF IT WEREN'T FOR THEIR GIFTS, HE WOULD NOT HAVE SLAIN MEDUSA OR SAVED ANDROMEDA.

PERSEUS!!

IS IT REALLY YOU?

MOTHER?! WHAT ARE YOU DOING HERE?

WELCOME BACK, PERSEUS. YOU ARE JUST IN TIME FOR A WEDDING.

MY MOTHER HAS REFUSED TO MARRY YOU, POLYDECTES. WHAT MAKES YOU THINK ANYTHING HAS CHANGED?

YOU AND YOUR MOTHER HAVE LIVED IN MY PALACE, EATEN MY FOOD AND ENJOYED MY PROTECTION FOR MANY YEARS, PERSEUS.

NOW IS HER CHANCE TO MAKE IT UP TO ME BY BECOMING MY WIFE!

WELL THEN, IF THERE'S GOING TO BE A WEDDING, I SHOULD GIVE YOU A WEDDING PRESENT!

39

DANAË WAS NEVER HAPPIER THAN THE DAY SHE MET ANDROMEDA. SHE WAS OVERJOYED THAT HER SON HAD FOUND SUCH A BRAVE AND BEAUTIFUL WIFE.

FOR A TIME, THEY ALL LIVED HAPPILY.

BUT THERE CAME A TIME WHEN DANAË BECAME HOMESICK FOR THE LAND OF HER BIRTH.

EVEN AFTER WHAT HE DID, I WOULD STILL LIKE TO SEE MY FATHER ONCE MORE, IF ONLY TO LET HIM KNOW THAT I HAVE FORGIVEN HIM.

I HAVE NO GRUDGE AGAINST HIM EITHER. IF ACRISIUS HADN'T SENT US AWAY, I MIGHT NEVER HAVE MET ANDROMEDA.

BESIDES, I WANT TO TELL HIM THAT HE HAS NOTHING TO FEAR FROM ME, NO MATTER WHAT THE ORACLE SAID.

USING THE SHIP THAT DICTYS HAD GIVEN THEM, THEY SAILED TO ARGOS.

WHEN THEY ARRIVED, THEY FOUND OUT THAT ACRISIUS HAD LEARNED OF THEIR JOURNEY AND HAD RUN OFF TO THE KINGDOM OF LARISSA. EVEN THOUGH YEARS HAD PASSED, HE WAS STILL AFRAID OF THE ORACLE'S PROPHECY.

THEY DECIDED TO FOLLOW ACRISIUS TO LARISSA, SO THEY COULD TELL HIM THAT IT WAS SAFE TO RETURN HOME.

SADLY, WHEN THEY ARRIVED, THEY LEARNED THAT THE KING OF LARISSA HAD JUST DIED. A SERIES OF GAMES WAS BEING HELD IN HIS HONOUR.

BECAUSE THE STORIES ABOUT PERSEUS HAD SPREAD FAR AND WIDE, THE PEOPLE OF LARISSA ASKED HIM TO PARTICIPATE IN THE GAMES.

I REALLY JUST WISH TO FIND MY GRANDFATHER, KING ACRISIUS OF ARGOS.

OF COURSE! OF COURSE! STILL, IT WOULD BE A GREAT TRIBUTE TO THE FALLEN KING ...

IF SUCH A FAMOUS HERO WOULD PARTICIPATE!

WHILE PERSEUS PREPARED TO COMPETE, DANAÉ AND ANDROMEDA FOUND A PLACE WHERE THEY COULD WATCH.

ACRISIUS CAUGHT A GLIMPSE OF HIS DAUGHTER AS SHE TOOK HER SEAT.

FEARING THAT HIS GRANDSON HAD COME TO KILL HIM, ACRISIUS TRIED TO FLEE.

HE DIDN'T REALIZE THAT PERSEUS WAS ON THE FIELD, ABOUT TO TAKE PART IN THE DISCUS THROW.

JUST AS PERSEUS MADE HIS THROW, A SUDDEN WIND BLEW IT ASTRAY.

AND SO THE PROPHECY WAS FULFILLED, EVEN THOUGH PERSEUS AND ACRISIUS BOTH TRIED TO PREVENT IT.

THOUGH PERSEUS WAS THE RIGHTFUL HEIR TO THE THRONE OF ARGOS, HE COULD NOT STAND TO RULE THERE AFTER CAUSING HIS GRANDFATHER'S DEATH. INSTEAD, HE WENT TO TIRYNS, WHERE HIS FATHER'S NEPHEW RULED.

THEN YOU AGREE TO TAKE THE THRONE OF ARGOS?

AND YOU WILL RULE HERE IN MY PLACE!

PERSEUS HAD A LONG LIFE. HE EXPANDED HIS KINGDOM, BUILDING A NEW CITY CALLED MYCENAE.

IT IS SAID THAT WHEN HE AND ANDROMEDA DIED, THE GODS TURNED THEM INTO STARS THAT WOULD SHINE FOREVER IN THE NIGHT SKY.

GLOSSARY

ACRISIUS the King of Argos, father of Danaë, and grandfather of Perseus

ADAMANTINE an unbreakable material

ANDROMEDA the princess of Ethiopia, whom Perseus rescues from the Kraken

ARGOS ancient Greek city where Perseus was born

ATHENA the Greek goddess of wisdom

CASSIOPEIA the wife of King Cepheus and mother of Andromeda

CEPHEUS the king of Ethiopia, husband of Queen Cassiopeia, and father of Andromeda

DANAË Perseus' mother

DICTYS a fisherman, brother of King Polydectes

GRAEAE the three blind witches from whom Perseus learns the location of the Gorgons

HADES the Greek god of the underworld

HERMES the messenger of the gods of Mount Olympus

MYCENAE an ancient Greek city founded by Perseus

ORACLE in ancient Greece, a priestess or other person through whom the gods were believed to communicate

PEGASUS a winged horse that arises from the blood of the slain Medusa

PERSEUS the son of Zeus and Danaë and king of Mycenae

PHINEUS Cepheus' kinsman, to whom Andromeda had been promised in marriage

POLYDECTES the king of Seriphus and brother of Dictys

POSEIDON the Greek god of the sea

SERIPHUS a small island kingdom located in the Aegean Sea

TIRYNS an ancient Greek kingdom, ruled by Perseus for many years

FURTHER READING, WEBSITES AND FILMS

Clash of the Titans. DVD. Directed by Desmond Davis. Hollywood, CA: Warner Brothers Entertainment, 1981. The story of Perseus' adventures is told in this classic early 1980s special effects extravaganza.

Limke, Jeff. *Theseus: Battling the Minotaur*. London: Lerner Books: Graphic Universe,
2009. Follow the adventures of another great Greek hero in this exciting volume from the Graphic Myths and Legends series. Theseus shows he is fit to be king of Athens by defeating several enemies, including the fearsome Minotaur, a monster who is half-man, half-bull.

Mythweb. http://www.mythweb.com/index.html. This site, with a searchable encyclopedia, provides readers with information on gods, goddesses, and places in Greek myth, including information about Perseus.

Shuter, Jane. *Ancient Greece (New Explore History)*. Oxford: Heinemann, 2005. This book shows readers why Greek fighters are so powerful, who the Greeks worshipped and why and what influence the Greeks have had on our buildings.

Storrie, Paul. *Hercules: The Twelve Labours*. London: Lerner Books: Graphic Universe, 2008

CREATING *PERSEUS: THE HUNT FOR MEDUSA'S HEAD*

Editor's Note: Sources conflict as to the home of Andromeda and her parents. Some say she was a princess of the ancient East African kingdom of Ethiopia – the setting chosen for this book. Others place her in the ancient city of Joppa, which is located near the modern-day city of Tel-Aviv, Israel. To retell this ancient story for modern readers, author Paul D Storrie consulted the two classic English-language anthologies of Greek tales—*The Age of Fable* (1859) by Thomas Bulfinch and *Mythology* (1942) by Edith Hamilton. Both books are based upon the classic works of ancient poets, including Ovid and Virgil. Artist Thomas Yeates based the story's visual details on reference books on ancient Greece and East Africa, as well as photos and scenes from classic films such as *Clash of the Titans*. Special thanks to Professor David Mulroy of the University of Wisconsin-Milwaukee, who lent his expertise to ensure that the story was accurate visually and historically.

INDEX

ABOUT THE AUTHOR AND THE ARTIST

PAUL D STORRIE was born and raised in Detroit, Michigan, USA. He has returned to live there again and again after living in other cities and states. He began writing professionally in 1987 and has written comics for Caliber Comics, Moonstone Books, Marvel Comics and DC Comics. Some of the titles he's worked on include *Batman Beyond*, *Gotham Girls*, *Captain America: Red, White and Blue* and *Mutant X*.

THOMAS YEATES began his art training in high school and continued at Utah State University and Sacramento State University, USA. Subsequently, he was a member of the first class at Joe Kubert's School, a trade programme for aspiring comic book artists in New Jersey, USA. Yeates has worked as an illustrator for DC Comics, Marvel, Dark Horse, and many other companies, drawing *Tarzan*, *Zorro*, *The Swamp Thing*, *Time Spirits*, *Captain America* and *Conan*. Yeates's many titles for the Graphic Myths and Legends series include *King Arthur: Excalibur Unsheathed*, *Arthur and Lancelot: the Fight for Camelot*, *Atalanta: the Race against Destiny*, *Robin Hood: Outlaw of Sherwood Forest* and *Odysseus: Escaping Poseidon's Curse*.

First published in the United States of America in 2008